RECORD OF PROFESSIONAL EXPERTISE

A Reflective Tool for Practice Nurses

RECORD OF PROFESSIONAL EXPERTISE

A Reflective Tool for Practice Nurses

JACKIE COOPER
RGN, ON, Plunket Cert (NZ), Family Planning Cert, Practice Nursing Cert, CertEd

Practice Nurse, West Yorkshire

Scutari Press
London

A division of Scutari Projects Ltd, the publishing company of the Royal College of Nursing.

First published 1994

British Library Cataloguing in Publication Data

Cooper, J.
Record of Professional Expertise
I. Title
362.173

ISBN 1 873853 08 4

Typeset by Dorwyn Ltd, Rowlands Castle, Hants
Printed and bound by Bell and Bain Ltd., Glasgow

PREFACE

This resource has been produced to take the mystery out of profiling by:

- using real life experiences, familiar to all practice nurses;
- making sense of the jargon;
- creating a flexible format which can be personalised, and
- encouraging recognition of the complexity of the role and anticipating the potential developmental opportunities for practice nurses.

The basic draft for this work was originally produced as a Certificate of Education project, with the support of Leeds Family Health Services Authority, who provided production and evaluation facilities. Various constructive comments and practical suggestions made by Practice Nurses who have evaluated the document have been of great value. Indeed, many of their contributions are now incorporated in the book.

Technical assistance found close to home, from neighbours who helped with research and word processing, was invaluable. Tolerance, understanding and practical sustenance given by my family at times when I have been preoccupied did not go unnoticed.

Encouragement and resource support from North Yorkshire FHSA made further development a reality, and they have provided 300 Practice Nurses with a copy.

Without the help of all those mentioned, this document would have been filed away 'in bud'. I am grateful that it has been given the chance to 'blossom' and for the sense of personal and professional growth this venture has given me.

JACKIE COOPER

CONTENTS

USES FOR A ROPE

This ROPE (Record of Professional Expertise) is specifically designed for Practice Nurses in the hope that it will be as useful as an ordinary rope in everyday situations, with particular value in certain circumstances.

In your mind's eye consider how ordinary rope might be used to hold something together or pull something along in a mundane sort of fashion, just as this ROPE can accompany you through your day to day work. The same piece of equipment, however, might prove invaluable in times of crisis. Consider the worth of ordinary rope, for example, in escaping from a burning building or rescuing someone who has fallen into a frozen lake. Your ROPE might be your means of escape if ever a professional dilemma occurs. The same ordinary equipment can also help in 'moving on to higher places', be it rock climbing or promotion.

As practice nurses we can use a ROPE to analyse, document and claim credit for our nursing practice. Incorporating the Royal College of Nursing Standards of Care framework, it is a means of ensuring quality service. As health professionals we need to apply our skills and knowledge, monitor the results of our activities and continuously strive for improvement and refinement. Accreditation of prior experiential learning may be possible with the help of a ROPE when considering community health care nurse status, or claiming credit for further education, or working towards the higher award.

A ROPE may provide evidence for Post-Registration, Education and Practice (PREP) documentation and help to prioritise any updating to be undertaken. When applying for new posts, a ROPE may be a useful insight for employers. Within present post or as part of study programmes, a research project may grow out of aspects of a nursing service needing improvement, as identified by a ROPE.

Using a ROPE can nurture a sense of 'the-yet-to-be-learned' while acknowledging the need to update 'that-which-is-already-known'. In this way Practice Nurses will not become complacent and patients will not receive only routine, habitual care.

A ROPE prompts us to consider: *Where am I now?* versus *Where do I want to be?*

WHAT MAKES A GOOD ROPE?

This document is a way of recording the reflections which help you to learn from your experience and practice. It is a means of identifying your strengths and the areas you want to develop which will help in setting your goals for the future.

There are information-gathering sections which will probably need regular updating in order to show progress in your professional work and which can be used as a basis for audit, among other things.

There are reflective diary-type sections which will help you to identify your direction based on what has been before. Some of the information will be useful to share with other people, but some may always remain private – this is your decision.

The process may prove to be difficult as it seems threatening and invasive to your inner self; keep remembering that it is for your benefit. You reveal only what you want to and the aim is to help yourself to keep growing as an individual, as well as a health professional. You will need to set aside time and decide that this is a worthwhile project if you are to produce a valid document. It needs to be the result of a careful, honest, consideration of yourself and your work. This is not something which you do once and for all: you will need to return to different sections many times.

It is important that you recognise and value what you already know. Recognise your good points, do not be shy about claiming what you are good at. If you keep telling yourself 'Oh, it's nothing', or 'I'm not particularly good at that', not only will you believe it; other people will think the same.

All the joys, sorrows, frustrations and achievements of your nursing career need to be acknowledged as part of your development. You have learned much of what you know from experiences and people, not only by attending courses and study days – be sure to make it all count!

REFLECTIONS

Perhaps you are one of those people who lay in bed and, before drifting off to sleep, rewind the tape in your mind of 'what happened today?'. As you are re-running it, you pause at certain points and think 'why did I do that?', 'what went wrong there?', 'phew, that worked out better than I thought it would', 'I got a good response from him for a change!'.

Sometimes you want to rewind the tape, to work out why things worked out that way, vowing never to make the same mistake again or hoping you will remember how to get it right again next time, before drifting off to sleep. On future occasions, you dig deep into your memory bank of 'ponderings', recalling when you have learned – this is a form of *reflection*.

Reflection turns **experience** into **learning**, which is likely to lead to **action**. This is how we can make our service to patients appropriate to their needs as individuals and to ensure a high standard of care and work in the most effective way, given the time and money available. It needs to be continuous, honest and realistic, all of which are likely to be what you do subconsciously, but what reflection also needs to be is *recorded*.

When reflecting on an experience, have an open mind and be willing to surprise yourself.

- Did it work well? If so, why? If not, why not?
- Who was involved?
- What led up to it?
- Did anything change as a result of it?
- What were your feelings at the time?
- What did you learn from it?
- What are your feelings now?

WRITING THINGS DOWN

By recording those activities which involve us each day at work, we can start to work out what we are good at, what we would like to do more, or do less of, and what we need in order to do things well.

You may prefer to work on this alone or enlist the support of a colleague. You might need to record certain activities on tape or paper in order to find out if you do them well.

Those odd half-hours of overtime and a few minutes for the drug representative during your lunch break could add up to a significant amount of time over a year; most of us tend to let it happen without realising how it accumulates. Producing a written account of your time might be a valuable exercise in itself, as a stress/time management exercise, and may even be the basis for an overtime payment claim!

Using your ROPE will, at least, be the basis for the professional 'pat on the back' you will give yourself if you keep a note of what you do, how you do it and why you do it that way. In other words, not simply letting it happen without realising what it amounts to.

Each nurse needs different skills and knowledge with job descriptions, responsibilities and expectations which vary greatly from practice to practice. If you feel that certain sections do not apply to your work, simply state 'skill not required in present circumstances'. Concentrate on those sections which matter to you now, using the blank charts to include aspects of your work not listed.

You might want to consider becoming involved in new areas by building up your knowledge and skills, when you see an unmet patient/practice need, or a gap in your professional profile. Keeping a diary account of work experiences is a good way of learning from mistakes, remembering what works well, keeping a reference to future events and to note your progress and adaptation over the years.

COMPETENCY CHARTS

This section will help you to identify what skills/knowledge you already feel you have and to decide which areas you want to develop. It is not intended to be a test, simply a framework to look at your day-to-day work and then make sense of it in terms of learning. If you discuss it with a colleague with whom you feel comfortable, it can highlight strengths and weaknesses you may not have noticed. You may want to return to update this section every 6–12 months. It will be interesting to note which aspects of your role gain or lose importance over time. For each competency, ask yourself:

- Am I consistently effective in this area?
- Could I improve my knowledge/skill?
- Why do I have difficulties with this?
- Although I am not practising this at present, should I try to include it in my work?

When considering making a claim of professional expertise within the different sections, it is important to realise that there are many varied ways in which your skills/knowledge can be recognised. In the column headed 'my claim can be supported by . . .' you need to be imaginative and realistic, offering evidence which genuinely shows your ability. Consider the following possibilities:

signed statements
protocol documents
teaching materials
meeting minutes
conference reports
referral letters
practice statistics
patient questionnaires
video-/audio-taped consultations
references/testimonials
projects/assignments
certificates – attendance
– achievement
– competence
audit summaries

Stating which kind of evidence and where it is kept would be appropriate, e.g. maintenance log book in treatment room; or you may keep paperwork, e.g. certificates, questionnaires used, etc., with your ROPE in clear plastic pockets so that everything is at hand for future reference.

Your claim may be something which is observed, received, participated in or supervised by someone. That person may be peer, colleague in the practice, mentor or patient. They may be willing to sign and perhaps comment on your claim in the right-hand column.

ACTION PLANS

Descriptions of events can be turned into a plan by working out what happened and why. Using your competency claims and reflections it may be useful to summarise your findings and write them on the action plan sheet provided. If you do not want to share the whole logbook with colleagues, employer, further education course assessors, etc., you might like to use these plans to demonstrate that you have been collecting information about yourself and have used it to highlight certain areas of your practice.

Do not tackle everything at once and try to plan action which will fit in with short- or long-term goals you may be working towards. Be realistic about the resources you will need and always set a review date for your chosen action. At the set date, look back on your progress so far, consider any further action and, if necessary, complete another action plan or new review date. Recognise the dynamic nature of practice nursing and accept that your action planning will never be finished – simply always moving on.

SETTING GOALS

Remember when Alice in Wonderland asked: 'Would you please tell me which way I ought to go from here?' The cat replied: 'That depends a good deal on where you want to get to!' (Carroll, L. (1865) *Alice's Adventures in Wonderland*).

Once you know where you are heading, what your target is and how you are going to get there, you might decide to write out your goals.

Long-term goals may be looking ahead a year or more, involving gaining knowledge, developing skills and leading to significant personal or professional changes of direction, for example:

- Studying for the Diploma of Professional Studies or a Degree
- Becoming a facilitator/mentor

- Taking responsibility for the nursing budget in the practice

Short-term goals may be based on the long-term plan and can be achieved within a few months. They should be realistic – do not set yourself up to fail, and be quite specific, so that you can see clearly in 6–12 months' time how close you are to reaching them.

You might take an aspect from the competency section to work on, decide how you will know when you have achieved the goal, undertake some training or change of practice and involve someone who can support you. 'Setting goals' pages are included and these may be worth discussing with someone who has perhaps supported your present claims or has been helpful in the reflective process.

This ROPE is yours – use it your way!

1

WORKPLACE PROFILE

WORKPLACE PROFILE

NURSE: ______________________________

Practice address: ______________________________

____

____

____

Telephone: ______________________________

PIN: ______________________________

RCN/MDU Membership No: ______________________________

Practice Manager: ______________________________

Senior Partner: ______________________________

Nurse Adviser: ______________________________

ESTABLISHMENT:

Patients: ______________________________

Doctors: ______________________________

Health Visitors: ______________________________

District Nurses: ______________________________

Pharmacy: ______________________________

Reception: ______________________________

NURSING STAFF:	Hours worked:	Qualifications:
Self:	________	________
Others:	________	________
	________	________
	________	________
	________	________
	________	________
	________	________
	________	________

HEALTH PROMOTION SERVICES OFFERED	**Nurses run?**	**Doctor involved?**	**Date update attended**	**Date last audited**
Asthma				
Diabetes				
Family Planning				
Stop Smoking				
Heart Disease Prevention				
Others				

EQUIPMENT IN USE	Daily	Weekly	Monthly	Less often
Sphygmomanometer: Aneroid Free-standing Wall-mounted				
Spirometer				
Peak Flow Meters				
Audiometer				
ECG Machine				
Nebuliser				
Smokalyser				
Vision Testing				
Urine Testing				
Glucometer				
Cholesterol Monitor				
Other				

POST REGISTRATION CURRICULUM VITAE		
Nursing qualifications	Date obtained	Where obtained
Examinations/FE qualifications		
Nursing posts held	From–To	Responsibilities/Achievements

POST REGISTRATION CURRICULUM VITAE		
Nursing qualifications	Date obtained	Where obtained
Examinations/FE qualifications		
Nursing posts held	From–To	Responsibilities/Achievements

ROLE SUMMARY		Daily	Weekly	Monthly	Less often
Health Screening:	Blood Pressure Urinalysis Venepuncture Obtaining swabs Cervical smears Bimanual pelvic exam Testicular self awareness Breast self awareness				
Health Education:	Individual Planned/Opportunistic Group				
Infection Control:	Sterilisation Equipment Use of gloves				
Family Planning:	Full range information Assist with IUCD fit Fit diaphragms Injection admin Monitor OCP users				
Dressings	Trauma Post surgery Leg ulcers				

ROLE SUMMARY	Daily	Weekly	Monthly	Less often
Ear Syringing				
Eye Irrigation				
Minor Surgery/Suturing: Preparation Assistance Documentation By self Suture Removal				
Immunisations: Childhood Tetanus Hep B Flu Travel				
Telephone Consultations: Random Protected time				
Computer updating: Searches				
Counselling: Part of general consultation Protected time				
Care of Emergency Equipment				
Elderly Screening				
Liaison/Referral Other Agencies				
Preparation of Prescriptions				

2 PRACTICE IN THE WORKPLACE

CONSIDERING MY PRACTICE IN THE WORKPLACE

I claim that I	My claim can be supported by	Supporting comments/ signed and dated
(a) Have knowledge of and comply with safety regulations		
(b) Keep maintenance records of equipment used		
(c) Systematically clean instruments and surfaces used for clinical procedures		
(d) Adhere to infection control measures suitable to work undertaken		
(e) Participate in development of Health and Safety policies		
(f) Ensure privacy during consultations		
(g) Maintain stock records and re-order as required		
(h) Work within allocated budget and plan for future funding requirements		
(i) Ensure familiarity with information technology in use in practice		

PRACTICE IN THE WORKPLACE		
I claim that I	My claim can be supported by	Supporting comments/ signed and dated

PRACTICE IN THE WORKPLACE		
I claim that I	My claim can be supported by	Supporting comments/ signed and dated

ACTION PLAN

DATE: ____________________________

HAVING CONSIDERED THE COMPETENCIES IN THIS SECTION, I REALISE THAT:

MY AIM IS:

THE ACTION I WILL TAKE:

RESOURCES I WILL NEED:

REVIEW PLANNED: ______________________________

LOOKING BACK:

NOW I WILL:

3
CONTINUING EDUCATION

CONSIDERING MY CONTINUING EDUCATION

This section is worth consulting regularly, to ensure that any updating/study days/courses which you attend are put to good use. You can use the blank chart and the diary section, further on in the pack, to demonstrate your ability to not only reflect on but also analyse (make sense of) any learning which takes place. These are skills now needed by us all in order to prove how we are progressing professionally.

Claim 'C' should be applied to all learning opportunities so that new knowledge is converted into quality care for patients, a quality service for the practice and professional development for you.

Accumulating credits is only worthwhile when measured against clinical or academic outcomes. You might like to give special thought to the framework of 10 key characteristics identified by the English National Board (ENB) for the higher award, as well as the preparation determined by the United Kingdom Central Council for Nursing, Midwifery and Health Visiting (UKCC) as necessary for Practice Nurses wanting to work as Community Health Care Nurses.

It is important to identify what has been learned, so that all experiences can be assessed and credit claimed. Being accepted for diploma/degree work will require evidence that you are ready to work at that level. You have probably felt, at times, that you were covering the same ground with some study days; make sure you are working to a new level as time and experience moves you on. Do not overlook the in-house training opportunities which may involve other members of the primary health care team in your practice. There are also distance learning packs which allow flexible study without disrupting the practice or your household too much.

However, *beware* – attending courses offering level one credits *ad infinitum* is a waste of a valuable you!

CONSIDERING MY CONTINUING EDUCATION

I claim that I	My claim can be supported by	Supporting comments/ signed and dated
(a) Maintain and develop my clinical knowledge		
(b) Identify my own training needs		
(c) Demonstrate application of newly acquired skills and knowledge		
(d) Investigate in-house/local/ national opportunities for updating and the necessary funding		

CONSIDERING MY CONTINUING EDUCATION		
I claim that I	My claim can be supported by	Supporting comments/ signed and dated

A SUMMARY OF COURSES/STUDY DAYS I HAVE ATTENDED

Date	Topics covered	Organised by	Hours	CATS rating

* All attendance certificates, useful notes/references, etc., could be kept together in this section.

A SUMMARY OF USEFUL READING MATERIAL

Title	Author	Subject covered	Helped me with

ACTION PLAN

DATE: ______________________

HAVING CONSIDERED THE COMPETENCIES IN THIS SECTION, I REALISE THAT:

MY AIM IS:

THE ACTION I WILL TAKE:

RESOURCES I WILL NEED:

REVIEW PLANNED: ______________________________

LOOKING BACK:

NOW I WILL:

4

PROFESSIONAL ACCOUNTABILITY

CONSIDERING MY PROFESSIONAL ACCOUNTABILITY

The UKCC *Code of Professional Conduct for the Nurse, Midwife and Health Visitor* includes issues relating to: accountability, competence, delegation, collaboration and confidentiality.

The UKCC *Scope of Professional Practice* considers application of knowledge, exercising judgement, enlarging/adjusting professional practice in more depth in relation to 'good practice' and 'standards of care'. It focuses on principles for practice instead of task-related issues. The role of 'identified' practitioner includes responsibilities for coordinating and supervising delivery of care, using a team approach and ensuring that support staff work within their level of competence. It may be that, in recognising an area where you are not able to practise to your full potential because of lack of educational opportunities, you will be able to identify the scope of your own practice more clearly. Recommendations contained in the UKCC *Council's Standards for Education and Practice following Registration* also need to be considered, particularly with regard to 'specialist' and 'advanced' practice.

These many influences on changes within the profession, closely relating to Practice Nursing, all need to be acknowledged when completing this section of the pack, which in itself is fairly task-orientated.

CONSIDERING MY PROFESSIONAL ACCOUNTABILITY

With regard to my role as a practice nurse **I claim that I**	**My claim can be supported by**	**Supporting comments/ signed and dated**
(a) Have negotiated and agreed to a written contract of employment, which implies a commitment to ongoing education		
(b) Have recently reviewed my job description which reflects a philosophy of teamwork		
(c) Promote research-based best nursing practice		
(d) Maintain good relationship and communication with patients, carers and staff		

CONSIDERING MY PROFESSIONAL ACCOUNTABILITY		
With regard to my role as a practice nurse **I claim that I**	**My claim can be supported by**	**Supporting comments/ signed and dated**
(e) Devise nursing care plans based on individual patient assessments		
(f) Evaluate the effectiveness of the care provided		
(g) Establish and manage the clinic work within the practice		
(h) Undertake the development of nursing policies within the practice		

CONSIDERING MY PROFESSIONAL ACCOUNTABILITY		
With regard to working as primary health care team worker **I claim that I**	**My claim can be supported by**	**Supporting comments/ signed and dated**
(a) Attend regular team meetings		
(b) Recognise individuals' roles within the team		
(c) Share aspects of patients' care with other appropriate team members		

CONSIDERING MY PROFESSIONAL ACCOUNTABILITY		
With regard to community resources **I claim that I**	**My claim can be supported by**	**Supporting comments/ signed and dated**
(a) Maintain an up-to-date directory of local voluntary organisations		
(b) Attend meetings related to voluntary and statutory work in the local area		
(c) Provide contact details for patients and carers, encouraging referral as needed		
(d) Use local health promotion material		

CONSIDERING MY PROFESSIONAL ACCOUNTABILITY

With regard to protocols **I claim that I**	**My claim can be supported by**	**Supporting comments/ signed and dated**
(a) Participate in the health needs assessment in the practice		
(b) Introduce appropriate protocol-led nursing care in the practice		
(c) Take responsibility for the nursing development of protocols using current literature and research findings		
(d) Participate in clinical audit which relates to the nursing service		

CONSIDERING MY PROFESSIONAL ACCOUNTABILITY		
With regard to time management **I claim that I**	**My claim can be supported by**	**Supporting comments/ signed and dated**
(a) Assess my workload priorities		
(b) Appreciate workloads of other team members		
(c) Request clerical help when needed		
(d) Plan realistic consultation times with regular audit		

CONSIDERING MY PROFESSIONAL ACCOUNTABILITY

With regard to patients' rights **I claim that I**	**My claim can be supported by**	**Supporting comments/ signed and dated**
(a) Respect patients' rights to confidentiality and choice		
(b) Deliver care which reflects a special regard for patients' emotional needs		
(c) Record information only when satisfied that those with access will maintain confidentiality		
(d) Document any reason for disclosure or withholding of information when considered in 'public interest'		
(e) Ensure adequate follow-up care whenever necessary		

PROFESSIONAL ACCOUNTABILITY		
I claim that I	My claim can be supported by	Supporting comments/ signed and dated

ACTION PLAN

DATE: ______________________

HAVING CONSIDERED THE COMPETENCIES IN THIS SECTION, I REALISE THAT:

MY AIM IS:

THE ACTION I WILL TAKE:

RESOURCES I WILL NEED:

REVIEW PLANNED: ______________________________

LOOKING BACK:

NOW I WILL:

5 HEALTH PROMOTION

CONSIDERING MY HEALTH PROMOTION RESPONSIBILITIES		
I claim that I	**My claim can be supported by**	**Supporting comments/ signed and dated**
(a) Keep a resource file of local facilities		
(b) Refer patients to other agencies		
(c) Attend appropriate updating		
(d) Maintain up-to-date displays		
(e) Document screening tests and results		

CONSIDERING MY HEALTH PROMOTION RESPONSIBILITIES

I claim that I	My claim can be supported by	Supporting comments/ signed and dated
(f) Maintain effective recall system		
(g) Make use of unplanned opportunities for lifestyle change and advice		
(h) Plan intervention to meet stated targets		
(i) Monitor the outcomes of intervention		

HEALTH PROMOTION		
I claim that I	My claim can be supported by	Supporting comments/ signed and dated

ACTION PLAN

DATE: ______________________________

HAVING CONSIDERED THE COMPETENCIES IN THIS SECTION, I REALISE THAT:

MY AIM IS:

THE ACTION I WILL TAKE:

RESOURCES I WILL NEED:

REVIEW PLANNED: ______________________________

LOOKING BACK:

NOW I WILL:

6

PREVENTATIVE CARE

CONSIDERING MY WORK IN PREVENTATIVE CARE		
With regard to womens' health **I claim that I**	**My claim can be supported by**	**Supporting comments/ signed and dated**
(a) Offer appropriate preconceptual counselling with relevant screening and information		
(b) Undertake cervical cytology/pelvic examination as per protocol		
(c) Teach breast self-awareness and provide information about screening service		
(d) Provide contraceptive services at a level which reflects degree of training undertaken		
(e) Advise and monitor menopausal management as per protocol		

CONSIDERING MY WORK IN PREVENTATIVE CARE

With regard to immunisation **I claim that I**	**My claim can be supported by**	**Supporting comments/ signed and dated**
(a) Follow detailed protocol signed by medical and nursing staff		
(b) Demonstrate safe storage of vaccines		
(c) Have authorisation to manage analphylactic shock in absence of medical staff		
(d) Complete all relevant documents		

CONSIDERING MY WORK IN PREVENTATIVE CARE

With regard to heart disease and stroke prevention **I claim that I**	**My claim can be supported by**	**Supporting comments/ signed and dated**
(a) Undertake opportunistic, targeted and patient-initiated screening		
(b) Follow agreed protocols regarding smoking/alcohol/ diet/exercise and stress management advice		

PREVENTATIVE CARE		
I claim that I	My claim can be supported by	Supporting comments/ signed and dated

ACTION PLAN

DATE: ______________________

HAVING CONSIDERED THE COMPETENCIES IN THIS SECTION, I REALISE THAT:

MY AIM IS:

THE ACTION I WILL TAKE:

continues overleaf

RESOURCES I WILL NEED:

REVIEW PLANNED: ______________________________

LOOKING BACK:

NOW I WILL:

7

CHRONIC DISEASE MANAGEMENT

CONSIDERING MY INVOLVEMENT WITH CHRONIC DISEASE MANAGEMENT

I claim that I	My claim can be supported by	Supporting comments/ signed and dated
(a) Follow protocols stating care for patients with hyper-tension/asthma/diabetes/ other, eg. depression, thyroid, epilepsy		
(b) Maintain disease register		
(c) Maintain recall register		
(d) Analyse outcome of care in practice population		
(e) Carry out necessary tests and investigations		
(f) Give up-to-date information		
(g) Have up-to-date knowledge of medications used in practice		

CHRONIC DISEASE MANAGEMENT		
I claim that I	My claim can be supported by	Supporting comments/ signed and dated

ACTION PLAN

DATE: ______________________________

HAVING CONSIDERED THE COMPETENCIES IN THIS SECTION, I REALISE THAT:

MY AIM IS:

THE ACTION I WILL TAKE:

continues overleaf

RESOURCES I WILL NEED:

REVIEW PLANNED: ______________________________

LOOKING BACK:

NOW I WILL:

8
ACUTE CARE

CONSIDERING MY RESPONSIBILITIES FOR ACUTE CARE IN THE PRACTICE		
With regard to carrying out investigations **I claim that I**	**My claim can be supported by**	**Supporting comments/ signed and dated**
(a) Ensure patient comfort and safety		
(b) Ensure safe disposal of sharps and dressings		
(c) Ensure protection of self and others by correct handling, labelling and transportation of specimens		

CONSIDERING MY RESPONSIBILITIES FOR ACUTE CARE IN THE PRACTICE		
With regard to emergency care **I claim that I**	**My claim can be supported by**	**Supporting comments/ signed and dated**
(a) Am regularly updated on recognition and treatment of cardiac arrest		
(b) Have access to all necessary drugs and equipment		
With regard to wound care (a) Have access to latest dressings and techniques		
(b) Demonstrate aseptic technique and maintain clinically safe environment		
(c) Refer to other team members for advice as required		

CONSIDERING MY RESPONSIBILITIES FOR ACUTE CARE IN THE PRACTICE		
With regard to surgical procedures **I claim that I**	**My claim can be supported by**	**Supporting comments/ signed and dated**
(a) Maintain stocks of instruments and equipment		
(b) Sterilise and maintain instruments as required		
(c) Inform patients about procedures and aftercare		
(d) Assist doctor, ensuring safety of patient, self and other staff		

ACUTE CARE		
I claim that I	My claim can be supported by	Supporting comments/ signed and dated

ACTION PLAN

DATE: ____________________________

HAVING CONSIDERED THE COMPETENCIES IN THIS SECTION, I REALISE THAT:

MY AIM IS:

THE ACTION I WILL TAKE:

continues overleaf

RESOURCES I WILL NEED:

REVIEW PLANNED: ______________________________

LOOKING BACK:

NOW I WILL:

9
DIARY OF SIGNIFICANT EVENTS

This section is a useful record of 'life's little lessons'. You know, those days when you are feeling as pleased as Punch or saying 'never again'! Briefly describe what happened and, when you have given it some thought, what you learned from the event. Writing it down will help to show you how you can use the experience and may act as a prompt for further training, a request for resources or building your self-esteem.

This will probably be a section which is private, so use it honestly, with the security of knowing that *you* are in control and you are using it as personal development.

DIARY

Date	What happened	What I learned	How I will use the experience?

DIARY

Date	What happened	What I learned	How I will use the experience?

DIARY

Date	What happened	What I learned	How I will use the experience?

DIARY

Date	What happened	What I learned	How I will use the experience?

DIARY

Date	What happened	What I learned	How I will use the experience?

DIARY

Date	What happened	What I learned	How I will use the experience?

DIARY

Date	What happened	What I learned	How I will use the experience?

10

ME, MYSELF, I

SELF-EVALUATION

The following questions and observations may help you to realise what aspects of your work are important to you.

- What occasion/event in the past year has been most satisfying for you?
- What made it so special?
- What occasion/event has been particularly difficult?
- What helped you to cope?
- What kind of activities do you avoid?
- Have you made any deliberate changes of direction which you did not anticipate?

You may recognise patterns in the way you work.

- You may know that you work best on your own with clear and open lines of communications
- You may prefer sharing responsibility with other team members
- You may have problems with 'making yourself heard' accurately at meetings, or understood on paper
- You may miss out on opportunities because 'you hesitate too much'
- You may feel overwhelmed because 'you tackle too many things at once'

ME, MYSELF, I

What do I know about myself?

(I believe in ______________ ; It is important to me that ______________ ;
I ought to ____________________ , etc.)

DATE:

ME, MYSELF, I

Positive aspects of my nursing practice:
(what have I done well, practice developments undertaken, innovation recognised, etc.)

Obstacles I have encountered:
(people/time/money/attitudes/life events, etc.)

ME, MYSELF, I

What do I want others to know about me?
(I am good at ____________ ; I have a problem with ____________ ;
I want to ________________ , etc.)

Aspirations for the future:
(e.g. plans for change, training to be undertaken, career move, etc.)

Priorities for professional/personal development:

I have/have not found it helpful to discuss my reflections and plans with an assessor/mentor/colleague/peer (delete roles *not* applicable)

whose support is acknowledged below:

Signed ______________________ Date ______________________

11

GOAL SETTING

DATE: ______________________

At present, the action plans I have completed will help me to achieve the following:

Short-term Goal(s) (eg. become better at ______________________
make a change in ______________________)

I hope to reach this stage by ______________________

My short-term goals will help me to achieve the following **Long-term Goal**:

I hope to reach this by ______________________

It would be useful to contact ______________ ( ) Tick when done
______________ ( )
______________ ( )
______________ ( )
______________ ( )

DATE: ____________________

At present, the action plans I have completed will help me to achieve the following:

Short-term Goal(s) (eg. become better at ____________________
make a change in ____________________)

I hope to reach this stage by ____________________

My short-term goals will help me to achieve the following **Long-term Goal**:

I hope to reach this by ____________________

It would be useful to contact ____________________ (   ) Tick when done
____________________ (   )
____________________ (   )
____________________ (   )
____________________ (   )

DATE: ____________________

At present, the action plans I have completed will help me to achieve the following:

Short-term Goal(s) (eg. become better at ____________________
make a change in ____________________)

I hope to reach this stage by ____________________

My short-term goals will help me to achieve the following **Long-term Goal**:

I hope to reach this by ____________________

It would be useful to contact ____________________ ( ) Tick when done
____________________ ( )
____________________ ( )
____________________ ( )
____________________ ( )

DATE: ______________________

At present, the action plans I have completed will help me to achieve the following:

Short-term Goal(s) (eg. become better at ______________________
make a change in ______________________)

I hope to reach this stage by ______________________

My short-term goals will help me to achieve the following **Long-term Goal**:

I hope to reach this by ______________________

It would be useful to contact ______________ ( ) Tick when done
______________ ( )
______________ ( )
______________ ( )
______________ ( )

DATE: ______________________

At present, the action plans I have completed will help me to achieve the following:

Short-term Goal(s) (eg. become better at ______________________
make a change in ______________________)

I hope to reach this stage by ______________________

My short-term goals will help me to achieve the following **Long-term Goal**:

I hope to reach this by ______________________

It would be useful to contact ________________ (   ) Tick when done
________________ (   )
________________ (   )
________________ (   )
________________ (   )